SEMA INSTITUTE OF YOGA
P.O.Box 570459
Miami, Florida, 33257
(305) 378-6253 Fax: (305) 378-6253

First U.S. edition 1997

The author is available for group lectures and individual counseling. For further information contact the publisher.

Ashby, Muata
The Story of Asar, Aset and Heru ISBN: 1-884564-31-3

Library of Congress Cataloging in Publication Data

1 Ancient Egypt 2 Juvenile literature, 3 Ancient Egyptian Myths, 4 Juvenile spirituality.

Cruzian Mystic Books

www.Egyptianyoga.com

Also by Muata Ashby

EGYPTIAN YOGA: THE PHILOSOP HY OF ENLIGHTENMENT
INITIATION INTO EGYPTIAN YOGA
MYSTICISM OF USHET REKHAT
EGYPTIAN PROVERBS
THEF NETERU: THE MOVEMENT OF THE GODS AND GODDESSES
THE CYCLES OF TIME
THE HIDDEN PROPERTIES OF MATTER
GOD IN THE UNIVERSE
THE MYSTICAL TEACHINGS OF THE AUSARIAN RESURRECTION
THE WISDOM OF MAATI
THE SERPENT POWER
EGYPTIAN TANTRA YOGA
THE BLOOMING LOTUS OF DIVINE LOVE
MEDITATION: THE ANCIENT EGYPTIAN PATH TO ENLIGHTENMENT
For more listings see the back section.

Sema
Institute of Yoga

Sema (↯) is an Ancient Egyptian word and symbol meaning *union*. The Sema Institute is dedicated to the propagation of the universal teachings of spiritual evolution which relate to the union of humanity and the union of all things within the universe. It is a non-denominational organization which recognizes the unifying principles in all spiritual and religious systems of evolution throughout the world. Our primary goals are to provide the wisdom of ancient spiritual teachings in books, courses and other forms of communication. Secondly, to provide expert instruction and training in the various yogic disciplines including Ancient Egyptian Philosophy, Christian Gnosticism, Indian Philosophy and modern science. Thirdly, to promote world peace and Universal Love.

A primary focus of our tradition is to identify and acknowledge the yogic principles within all religions and to relate them to each other in order to promote their deeper understanding as well as to show the essential unity of purpose and the unity of all living beings and nature within the whole of existence.

The Institute is open to all who believe in the principles of peace, non-violence and spiritual emancipation regardless of sex, race, or creed.

About the author and editor:
Dr. Muata Abhaya Ashby

About The Author

Reginald Muata Ashby holds a Doctor of Philosophy Degree in Religion, and a Doctor of Divinity Degree in Holistic Healing. He is also a Pastoral Counselor and Teacher of Yoga Philosophy and Discipline. Dr. Ashby is an adjunct faculty member of the American Institute of Holistic Theology and an ordained Minister. Dr. Ashby has studied advanced Jnana, Bhakti and Kundalini Yogas under the guidance of Swami Jyotirmayananda, a world renowned Yoga Master. He has studied the mystical teachings of Ancient Egypt for many years and is the creator of the Egyptian Yoga concept. He is also the founder of the Sema Institute, an organization dedicated to the propagation of the teachings of Yoga and mystical spirituality.

Karen Clarke-Ashby "Vijaya-Asha" is the wife and spiritual partner of Muata. She is an independent researcher, practitioner and teacher of Yoga, a Doctor in the Sciences and a Pastoral Counselor, the editor of Egyptian Proverbs and Egyptian Yoga by Muata.☥

Sema Institute
P.O. Box 570459, Miami, Fla. 33257
(305) 378-6253, Fax (305) 378-6253
©1997

DEDICATION

To the Child Heru
who is the heart of every boy and girl in the universe.

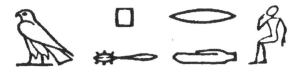

"Heru p-cha-rd   Heru the child"

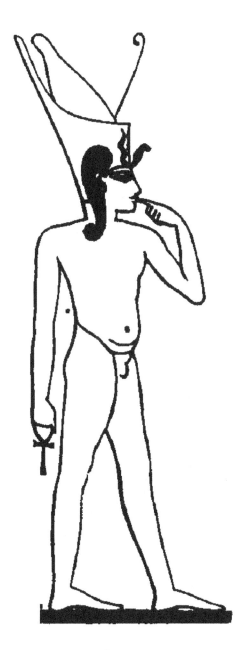

Attention Parents

This book may be used with *The Parents Guide To The Ausarian Resurrection Myth*: *How to Teach Yourself and Your Child the Principles of Universal Mystical Religion.*

$5.99 U.S.

The ſtory of Aſar, Aſet and Heru

(Osiris, Isis, and Horus)

Ancient Kemetic Terms and Ancient Greek Terms

In keeping with the spirit of the culture of Kemetic Spirituality, in this volume we will use the Kemetic names for the divinities through which we will bring forth the Philosophy of the Prt M Hru. Therefore, the Greek name Osiris will be converted back to the Kemetic (Ancient Egyptian) Asar (Ausar), the Greek Isis to Aset (Auset), the Greek Nephthys to Nebthet, Anpu to Anpu or Apuat, Hathor to Hetheru, Thoth or Hermes to Djehuti, etc. (see the table below) Further, the term Ancient Egypt will be used interchangeably with "Kemit" ("Kamit"), or "Ta-Meri," as these are the terms used by the Ancient Egyptians to refer to their land and culture.

Ancient Kemetic Terms and Ancient Greek Terms

Kemetic (Ancient Egyptian) Names	Greek Names
Amun	Zeus
Ra	Helios
Ptah	Hephastos
Nut	Rhea
Geb	Kronos
Net	Athena
Khonsu	Heracles
Set	Ares or Typhon
Bast	Artemis
Uadjit	Leto
Asar (Ausar)	Osiris or Hades
Aset (Auset)	Isis or Demeter
Nebthet	Nephthys
Anpu or Apuat	Anubis
Hetheru	Hathor (Aphrodite)
Heru	Horus or Apollo
Djehuti	Thoth or Hermes
Maat	Astraea or Themis

A long, long time ago the whole universe was an ocean. Its name was NU. There were no stars, no planets and no people anywhere around.

Everything was the same, everything was together, everything was one.

But there was someone sleeping in that ocean. Who was it?

It was RA who was sleeping there. RA is the Creator, the father of all fathers and the mother of all mothers.

Many people around the world have a name for the Creator. Some people call the Creator Allah, some use the name God the Father, some use the name Buddha, some use the name Krishna. In the African land of Ancient Egypt they used the name Ra.

RA was dreaming about all of the wonderful things he could imagine, the stars and planets, people, animals, plants and everything in the world he could create.

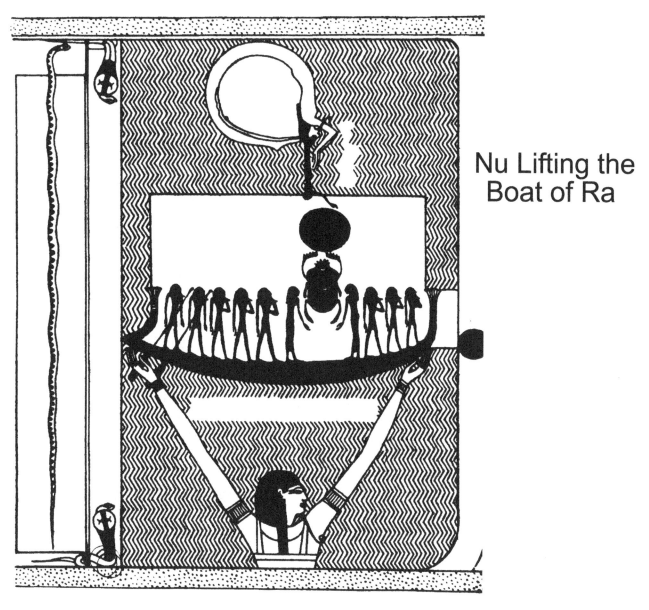

Nu Lifting the Boat of Ra

So that very day RA decided to create the universe.

But how can he create the universe and where would he do this creation?

RA thought within himself: "Nothing exists except me and my oceanlike body, Nu. I will transform my my ocean-like body (Nu) into Creation. I will use my ocean like self and turn myself into everything that will be."

So RA emerged from the ocean in a beautiful boat. He emerged in the form of a beetle which is the Ancient Egyptian symbol of Creation. The boat was held up by the ocean god Nu.

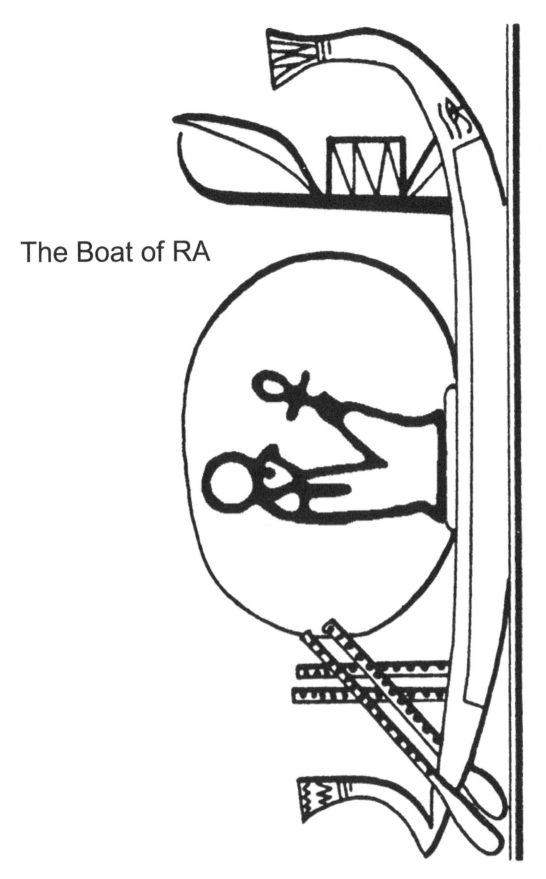

The Boat of RA

RA The Creator

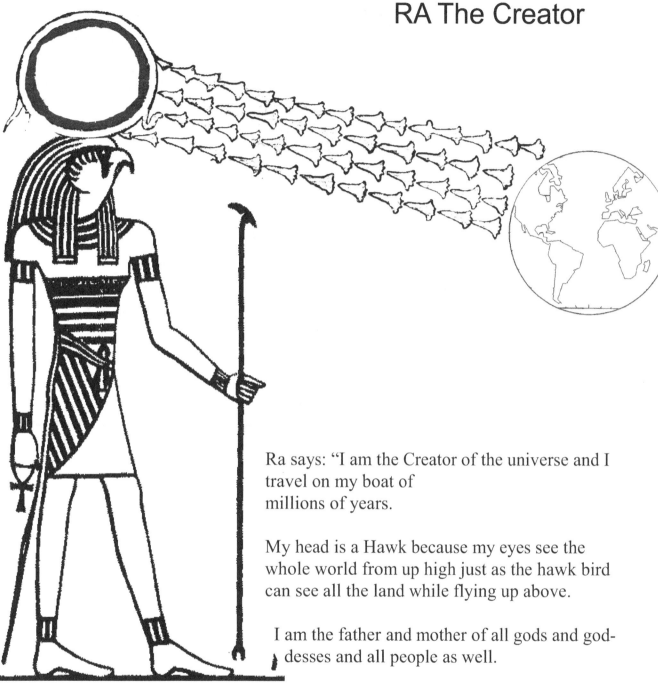

Ra says: "I am the Creator of the universe and I travel on my boat of millions of years.

My head is a Hawk because my eyes see the whole world from up high just as the hawk bird can see all the land while flying up above.

I am the father and mother of all gods and goddesses and all people as well.

As my eye, the sun, travels in the sky I give light and energy to all the world through my sunrays which are as soft as lotuses. With my sunrays I touch everyone and bless them with life and warmth so they can remember me every day. From the sky I look at all of my children on earth."

MAAT

Maat means:
Truth
Justice
Righteousness
Order
and
Harmony

But RA then said: "How will I take care of Creation because if I make something it might fall apart?" There must be some order to Creation. Water should run downhill instead of up and fire should burn up and not down. Otherwise, there will be confusion in the world. I will create my children, gods and goddesses, who will take care of Creation for me."

So RA thought: "Hmm," "I will create a daughter, a goddess and her name will be MAAT. It will be her responsibility to keep order, harmony, truth and righteousness in everything that I will create. Anybody who follows MAAT will live in peace and happiness."

People should be honest, kind and good to each other. If they forget about Maat they will get into trouble. If they think about Maat they will be in harmony with all the universe and they will be always happy and free.

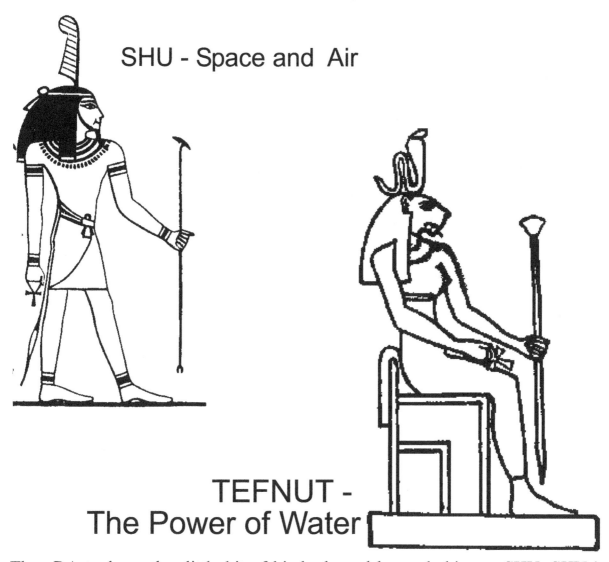

SHU - Space and Air

TEFNUT -
The Power of Water

Then RA took another little bit of his body and he made his son SHU. SHU is space and air. SHU is the space around you and this space contains air. SHU is also the breeze that blows. SHU allows you to be able to breathe.

Take a minute and breathe in deeply and feel how SHU is giving you strength.

Then RA took another little bit of his body and he made his daughter TEFNUT with it. TEFNUT represents moisture, such as when it rains. Rain allows plants to grow and it brings water for people to live.

TEFNUT is the powerful strength which is in the ocean of creation and she is the source of vitality for all living things.

NUT

RA sailing over the back of NUT

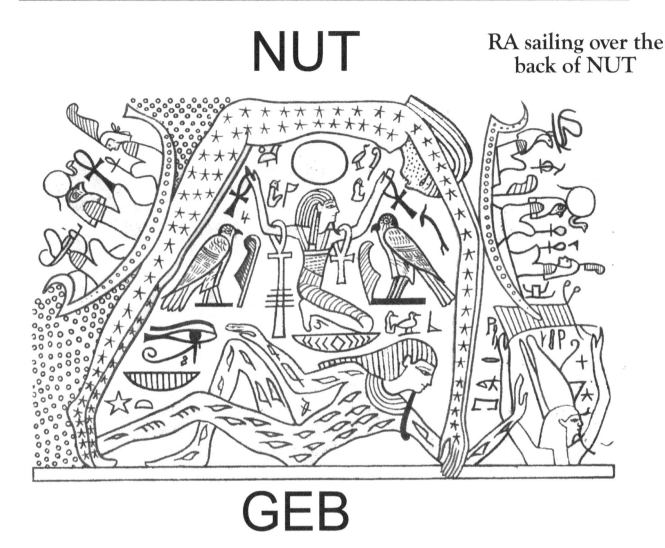

GEB

Then RA took another piece of his ocean-like body and created another daughter, the goddess NUT. NUT is the heavens. RA put the stars, the planets, the galaxies, and countless other worlds within her body, the sky, like beautiful ornaments.

Then RA said: "People will need a solid place if they want to walk, so then RA took another little bit of his ocean-like self and created GEB, the earth."

And RA said: "Now I will sail my boat over NUT, the sky, every day and I will shine on GEB, the earth, every day."

MAAT is RA'S closest daughter. She sits with him in the boat of millions of years and she has a feather on her head.

The feather symbolizes truth and order and MAAT keeps all things in the universe in their proper place.

MAAT makes sure that the earth stays in its place and that the stars in the sky stay in their places.

Look up in the sky and see how MAAT is doing her work right now.

The boat of RA is the sun in the sky. As it ries up in the morning and sets in the evening ,MAAT is with him. She keeps everything in its place as RA creates the new day every day.

Look up and see the sky... smile at NUT!

Look down and see the earth... smile at GEB!

Look all around you and between NUT and GEB and see the space with air in between the sky and the earth. This is SHU... so smile at SHU!

It is a special feeling to know that you are surrounded by the children of RA, the Creator.

So RA and his children are with you all the time... wherever you are.

Then RA said: "Now I will go to the continent of Africa which is on the body of my son GEB and make the land of KAMIT (Egypt) so that my children, the gods and goddesses and all people can have a city to live in."

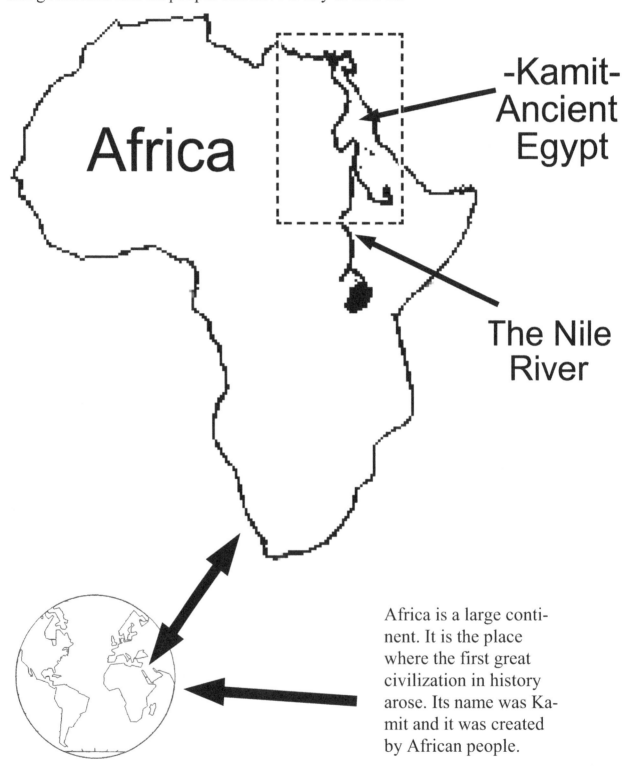

-Kamit-
Ancient
Egypt

The Nile
River

Africa is a large continent. It is the place where the first great civilization in history arose. Its name was Kamit and it was created by African people.

ASET

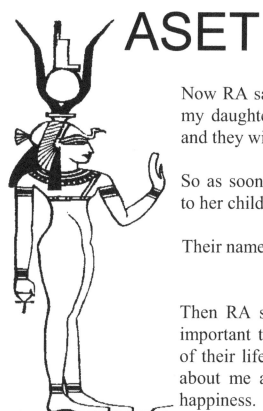

ASAR

Now RA said: "The world is here so now my daughter NUT will have her children and they will live all over the universe."

So as soon as RA spoke NUT gave birth to her children.

Their names were: ASAR and ASET, SET and NEBTHET.

Then RA said: "NUT'S children will be important to all people because the story of their life will teach all people on earth about me and how to live in peace and happiness.

SET

NEBTHET

Ra Creates Men and Women and Children

RA, the Great Supreme Being, decided: "I will now create men, women and children to live on earth. They will be my children, but it will hurt me because they will go and live on the earth and they will forget me for a long time."

So RA began to cry and from the tears of RA men and women on earth were formed. People in all of the countries all over the earth were created by RA as he cried.

So no matter how different people look and no matter where they come from they all have the same Creator: RA, and he loves them all equally.

TEHUTI

SESHETA

Then RA said: "If All Creation is made from my body, how will I talk with my children who will live on earth?"

RA thought again and said: "I will create two more children of mine so that through them I can talk with everyone and bring them my wisdom and hear their prayers."

So the god DJEHUTI (Djehuti) the goddess SESHETA, who bring the wisdom of writing and knowledge to the world, were created.

So every time people learn new things it is because RA is sending them wisdom through DJEHUTI and SESHETA.

One day RA found out that even though MAAT was trying to keep the world running with order, justice and harmony that some men and women did not understand how to live in peace.

Ra saw that some people would act badly to other people.

Sometimes people would yell at others and tell lies.

Sometimes people would fight with others.

Some people had forgotten about Ra and they forgot that all people have the same Creator and that all people are brothers and sisters.

So RA thought: "Hmm, I love my children, the people of the earth so I will send my grandson ASAR and my granddaughter ASET to show the whole world how people should live in harmony, peace and love according to the teachings of MAAT."

People fighting

ASAR and ASET as King
and Queen of Ancient Egypt

ASAR was the older and wiser than SET so he became the king of Ancient Egypt.

ASET became the queen and together they, ASAR and ASET, traveled all over the earth, spreading wisdom and joy throughout the land.

ASAR and ASET Travel Around The World

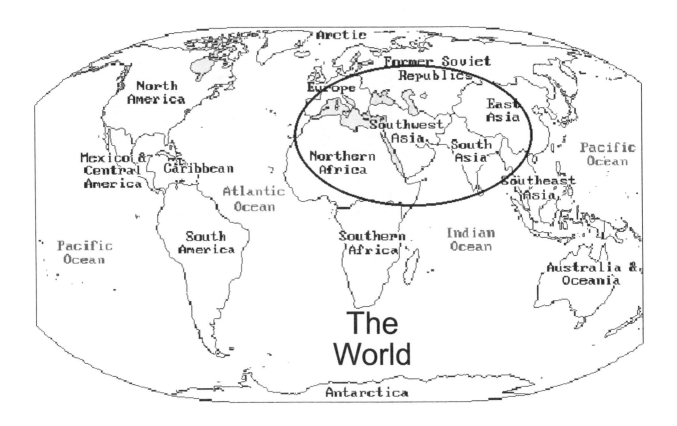

ASAR and ASET traveled all over Africa, Europe, India and China and even to-day the people of those places remember them with love.

One day ASAR returned to KAMIT from a trip around the world and every one in Ancient Egypt danced and rejoiced.

Dancing and rejoicing

People from all over the land danced and sang in honor of Asar and Aset.

SET

Everyone was happy except one person.

That person was SET.

SET was jealous and greedy.
He was not happy with the job that RA gave him. SET wanted to have his brother ASAR'S job. He wanted to be the king.

So he began to think bad thoughts about ASAR: "If I get rid of ASAR, I can be the king."

SET became so angry, greedy and full of hate that he decided to kill ASAR. So one day when nobody was around he killed ASAR and then threw ASAR'S body into the Nile River and it floated away.
Nobody knew where to find it.

NEBTHET and ASET

When ASET and NEBTHET found out what happened they began to cry.

ASET sobbed: "I must find the body of ASAR and bring it back to KAMIT. Who will take care of the people of the earth if the good king ASAR has been killed?

How will people learn to be good and caring to each other if ASAR is not here to teach them?

How will we live and be happy if ASAR is not here to keep us company with his wonderful aroma of love, peace and goodness? Oh my dear sister NEBETHET, we must find the body of ASAR and bring it back to KAMIT and I must pray over it!"

NEBETHET said: "Oh my dear sister, you have spoken well. We must find the body of ASAR and bring it back at once!"

So ASET and NEBTHET went out to find the body of ASAR.

ASET

With the help of the gods APUAT and SEBEK, ASET and the NEBTHET searched all over the world for the body of ASAR.

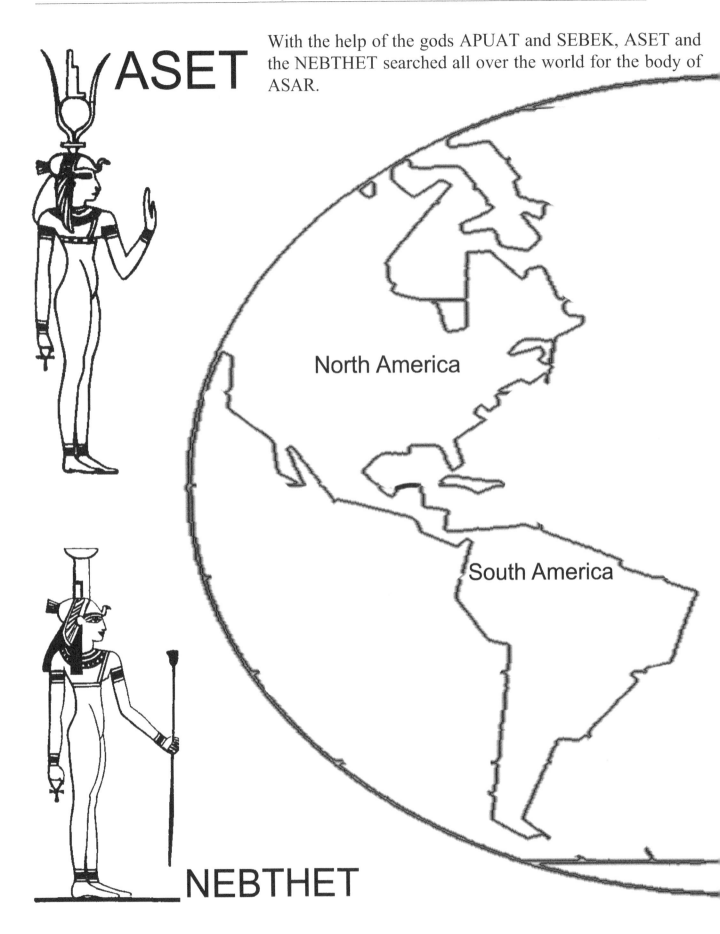

North America

South America

NEBTHET

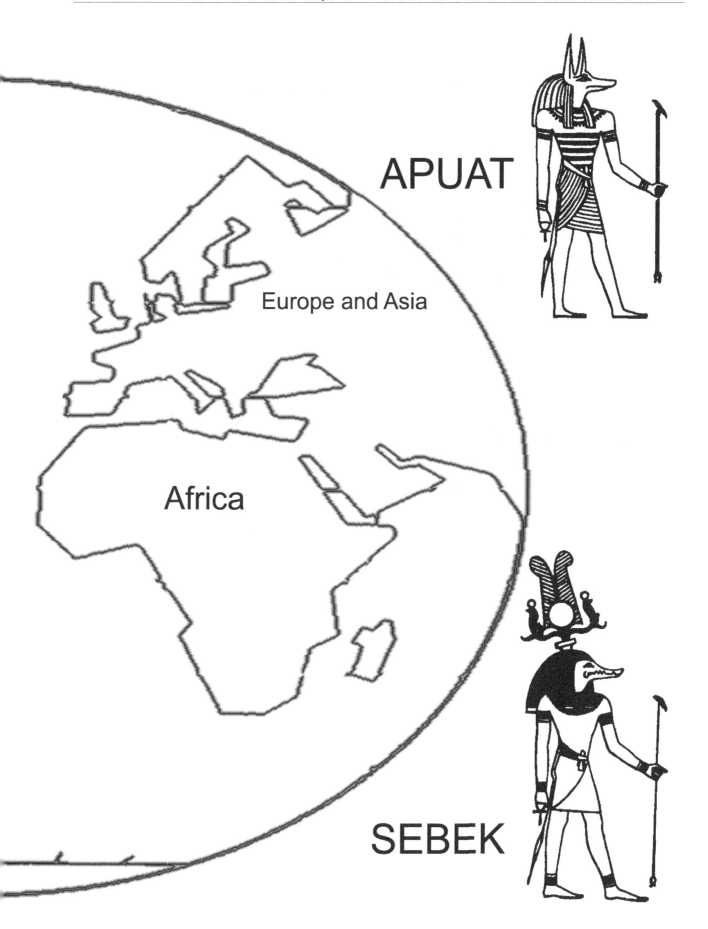

APUAT

Europe and Asia

Africa

SEBEK

The Body of Asar Grows into a Tree

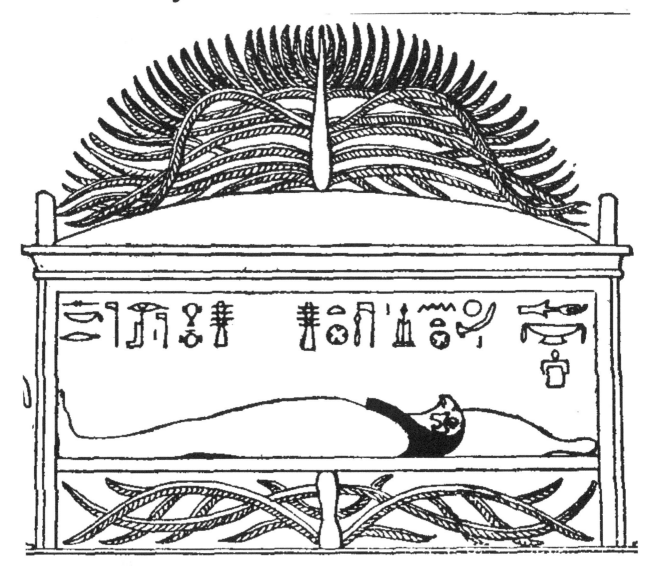

ASET found the body of ASAR in the land of Syria. It had grown into the form of a tree. The king of Syria had liked the smell of the tree so much that he had it cut and made it into a pillar for his palace.

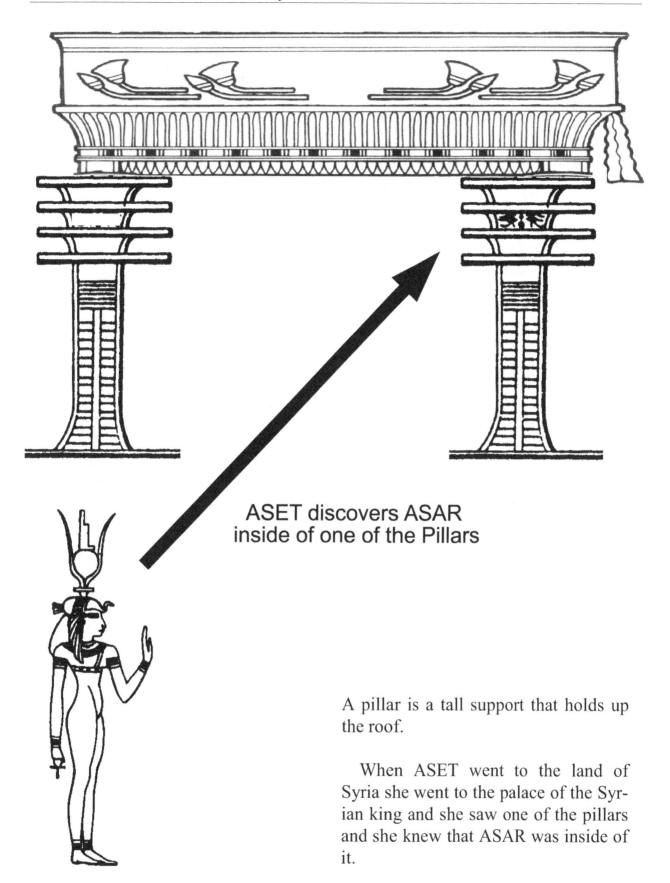

ASET discovers ASAR
inside of one of the Pillars

A pillar is a tall support that holds up the roof.

When ASET went to the land of Syria she went to the palace of the Syrian king and she saw one of the pillars and she knew that ASAR was inside of it.

ASET asked the king of Syria to give her the pillar which had ASAR inside of it.

She said: "Gracious King, my husband suffered a great injustice. He was placed in a coffin and dumped in the Nile river by the evil Set. I have been searching for it ever since that time. The coffin came to your shore and turned itself into a tree with a beautiful aroma. This wonderful aroma is the sweetness of my husband ASAR. His compassion and goodness are like a cool breeze in the summer and everyone is drawn to him because of this great aroma of goodness and peace.

The Syrian king said "Yes I will gladly give you this wonderful smelling pillar which has ASAR inside of it."

ASET prays over the dead body of ASAR

ASET opened up the pillar and found the mummy of ASAR. His body was lifeless. It was wrapped in bandages.

So ASET prayed and prayed over it with all her love and all her devotion.

Then ASAR opened his eyes and said: "My dear ASET, your love, devotion and wisdom have brought me back to life one more time so that we may have a child together. His name will be HERU and he will someday become the King of KAMIT and he will establish righteousness and truth in all the land again."

So Asar rose up from between the wings of Aset with his crook scepter and his flail scepter. He was a king again and he had overcome death.

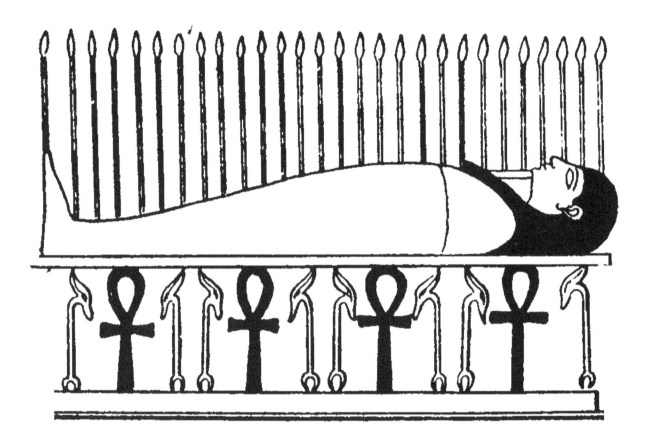

Then the Spirit of ASAR left his body to become the king of the land of the afterlife while ASET stayed on earth.

Since the heart of ASAR was pure, because he always had good thoughts, his body became the source of life and strength for all plants and trees. This is why plants and trees grow and produce food for all people.

The land of the afterlife is where the Spirit of all people goes after they die.

So it is because of ASAR that all plants grow and plants provide oxygen for people and animals to breathe, food for people and animals to eat and wood for people to make houses to live in.

Aset's belly began to grow because a baby was growing there. It was her baby HERU.

In a short time HERU was born.

With the help of DJEHUTI and AMUN, the soul of RA, ASET brought a baby into the world. ASET named him HERU. When HERU was born, all people all over the world were happy because they knew that one day he would save them from the selfish Set. All people danced and sang praises.

ASET taught HERU many things. She taught him about how RA created the universe, the gods and goddesses, people and the world.

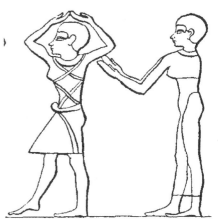

ASET taught him about how his father, ASAR, was the king, and how he traveled all over the world to spread peace and joy by showing people how to be kind to each other and to the earth.

When SET found out that HERU had been born, SET got very angry!

SET began to think bad thoughts again: "If HERU grows up the world will want him to be king because he is the son of ASAR and he is good and true. I want to be the king forever so I can't let HERU grow up."

Then SET said: "I will find HERU and I will kill him as I killed his father ASAR."

When ASET heard this she said: "I must take HERU to a place that is safe, away from SET, until HERU grows up."

So ASET ran away with HERU to a safe place, with the help of the scorpion goddess SELKET, and her seven scorpion friends, to protect HERU from harm.

ASET suckling and nurturing HERU

Heru eats vegetables and fruits

HERU and the Spirit of ASAR

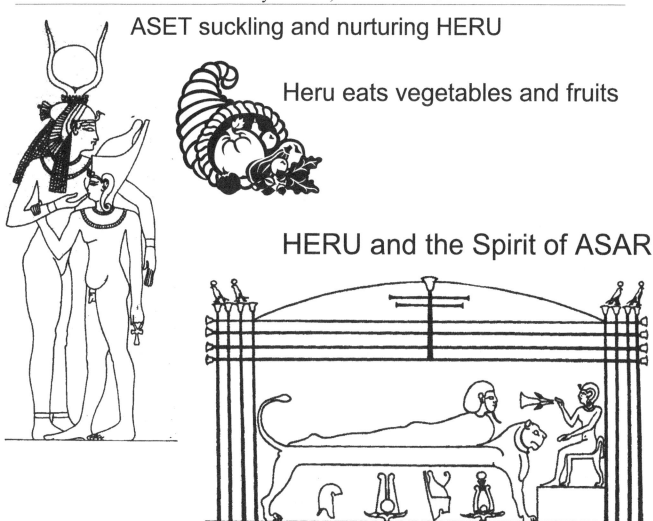

HERU asked ASET: "Mother, who am I and where do I come from?"

ASET answered: "HERU, my son, you, all people and all of the gods and goddesses come from the Spirit of RA and you are a special child because you will bring justice and truth to the world!"

ASET also taught HERU that he should always be good and true, and never tell lies or think bad thoughts about others.

As HERU grew up, ASET fed him vegetables and fruits to make him strong and healthy. HERU'S favorite food was lettuce.

ASET and the Spirit of ASAR taught HERU about justice and goodness. ASAR and ASET told HERU that he would one day challenge his uncle SET because SET was an evil king and did not teach the people of the world how to be good.

The gods and goddesses taught Heru the special exercises which will make him become strong and healthy for the challenges of life. These exercises are known today as Tjef Neteru Sema Paut YOGA exercises.

ASET told HERU that SET was selfish and all he cared about was himself. HERU grew up to be strong and caring for all people and all creatures.

HERU thought: "Soon I will go to SET and tell him to stop acting selfishly and stop hurting all the people."

Then one day HERU was old enough, he went to his uncle SET and told him: "You are selfish because you only care about yourself and you hurt people with your bad words and your wrong actions."

SET replied: "You are a little boy and I do not have to listen to you. I am the king and that is all I care about now."

HERU faces SET

HERU said: "I am young but I know the truth! You cannot be the king because you are not following the rules of MAAT. You are not the right king of Egypt. You killed my father and stole his things. This is not right. So give back everything you stole and say you are sorry for what you did."

SET said: "I do not care what you say. I will not give up what I stole."

HERU battles with SET
with the help of ASET

SETchanged his body
into a Hippopotamus

Then HERU said: "If you do not stop being bad and hurting people I will have to fight you."

Since SET did not want to follow the path of goodness HERU asked his mother ASET to help.

So the battle between HERU and SET began.

So the battle between HERU and SET began.

HERU sitting on a rock with his eyes hurting.

HERU and SET wrestled and fought but neither could win.

SET threw dirt in HERU'S eyes.

HERU could not see anything anymore.

HERU'S eyes hurt so much that he ran away. He went to a quiet place where he could be all alone and think about his problem.

He sulked and sobbed and he thought that he was alone.

HATHOR comes to help HERU.

HERU thought within himself: "How can I win against SET to stop his evil if he is as strong as I am."

Then the goddess HETHERU appeared. HETHERU is another daughter of RA. She is the light of the sun and the cousin of HERU.

HETHERU said: "My dear HERU. I have come to heal your right eye. Let me touch it with my power and you will see again.

You must look within yourself and know that I am the strength of the sun and I am in your heart. Then you will have the strength to face SET again."

DJEHUTI comes to help HERU.

Then the god DJEHUTI appeared and said: "Oh HERU, I have brought you wisdom and peace of mind to heal your left eye."

DJEHUTI said to HERU: "Always remember that the way to face bad people is with calm and not with anger. If you become angry you will not know what to do when the time comes. SET is not your real enemy, so do not become angry with him.

HERU asked: "What do you mean?"

SET is your uncle. He is acting badly because he is sick with the diseases of greed, hatred and anger. He has forgotten that his spirit comes from RA and that all people are his brothers and sisters. He became selfish and does not care for anybody but himself. So you must help him remember by letting him know when he is acting badly.

Then HERU asked: "How can I help SET?"

DJEHUTI answered: "If you want to help people who are doing bad things and saying bad things, you must stay calm, tell the truth and show them the right way to act. Always remember MAAT!"

HERU and SET
talk to the court of
gods and goddesses.

HERU went to SET again and said: "I have returned to face you once more! Let's go to the Court of gods and goddesses and see what they say."

So HERU and SET went in front of RA and the court of gods and goddesses.

HERU said: "SET killed my father and stole the kingdom. This is not right."

SET said: " HERU is too young to be king. I should be the king. Besides, I am strong and I won't give up being the king no matter what you say. I can beat up anyone who does not agree with me."

The court of gods and goddesses could not decide what to do, so they sent a letter to the goddess Net.

The Goddess Net.

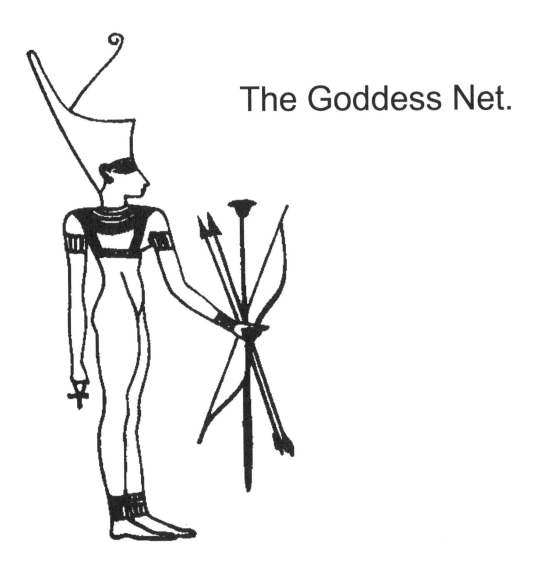

Net is the goddess of power and positive action.

When she received the letter from the court of gods and goddesses, she said:

"What is this injustice! How can it be right for SET to kill ASAR and then steal the kingdom away from HERU?

I say that HERU should be the king and that SET should not! The truth must always win over lies!"

The god DJEHUTI
writes a letter to the Spirit of ASAR.

The court of gods and goddesses were still not sure of what to do since SET was yelling at them and threatening them so they could not think clearly.

SET yelled: "If you do not allow me to be the king, I will hurt all of you and make you sorry! I should be the king and anyone who says otherwise will feel my anger."

SET was acting like a big bully.

The court of gods and goddesses decided to send a letter to the Spirit of ASAR in the kingdom of the afterlife to see what he thought should be done.

ASAR-SEKER

When the Spirit of ASAR, in his form as SEKER, the god of the afterlife, received the letter, he right away began to write back to the court of the gods and goddesses:

ASAR-SEKER wrote:

"Dear Court of gods and goddesses, think about what happened to me. SET killed my body and then stole the kingdom away from my son HERU. Is this right? SET is selfish and he does not care for people as I did.

You are the court that upholds truth and justice on earth. You must do what is right. Otherwise, there will be no peace and order in the world or in the kingdom of the afterlife."

SET

When the court of the gods and goddesses received the letter from ASAR, they decided that HERU should be the king of Egypt and that SET should take back his place of serving RA by protecting RA'S boat from the serpent of ignorance.

SET did not want to do this but he saw that HERU was not afraid of him.
SET knew that HERU would never give up fighting for the truth.

SET realized that HERU would never become angry or confused. This made HERU more powerful because he had the help of MAAT, TEHUTI, HETHERU, ASET and all of the other gods and goddesses.

SET also knew that he could never trick HERU and make him give up MAAT.

So SET said: "I now realize the injustice which I have done. I ask you all to forgive me and I bow to the feather of MAAT."

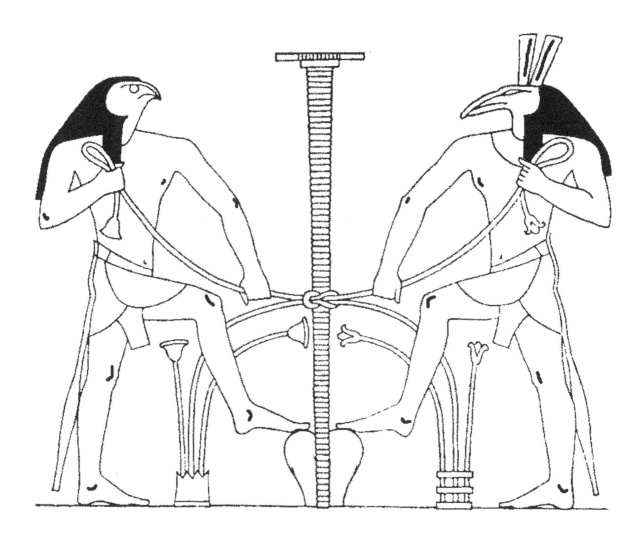

Now that everything was settled Heru and Set became friends. So they tied a knot on the symbol of unity, *SMA,* with lotus plants and papyrus plants and pledged to never hurt each other ever again. Both Heru and Set had achieved unity with their higher, true selves so they were very happy.

Heru said, "From now on the *SMA* (SEMA) symbol will be a sign for all people who want to practice unity and harmony with other people and with my father Asar and with my grandfather Ra. Any person who practices goodwill, truth, justice, peace and love can use this symbol so that the world may know that they are bringing harmony to the world and that they come in peace."

Set said, "Heru, you have spoken well.
I agree with you. Let this be a symbol for all good things.
Dua Sma! Dua Sma! Dua Sma! Dua Sma!
(Hail Unity, Hail Unity, Hail Unity, Hail Unity)"

Now HERU became strong and powerful in his name "HERU-UR."

SET said to HERU-UR: "I now see that RA gave me a perfect job, to protect his boat against the serpent of darkness which is always trying to bring ignorance, selfishness, anger, hatred and greed to the world.

The serpent of darkness always tries to stop the light of RA from shining on the world with love, peace and goodness.

This is my rightful place, to serve RA with all of my powers.

Everybody has a rightful place in the world and this place is mine.

HERU-UR, your rightful place is as king of KAMIT.

So may you live in HETEP (peace) for ever and guide the people of the world so that they may always act with MAAT. Then they too will be able to find their rightful place and discover happiness and joy in their life on earth until they go to join ASAR in the afterlife!"

Dua HERU-UR!
(I salute you HERU, king of KAMIT!)"

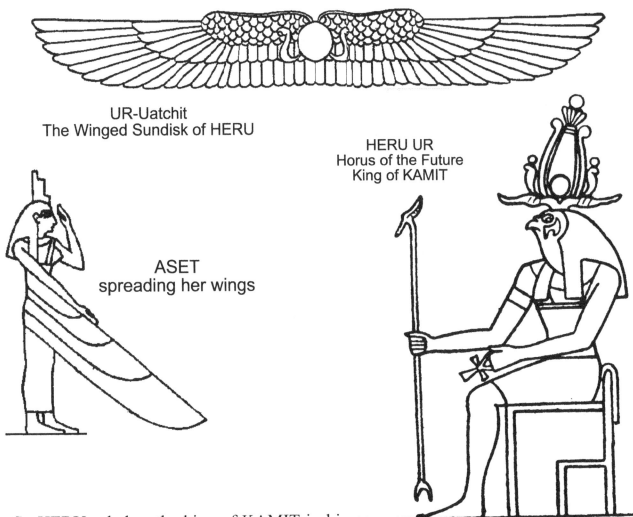

UR-Uatchit
The Winged Sundisk of HERU

HERU UR
Horus of the Future
King of KAMIT

ASET
spreading her wings

So HERU ruled as the king of KAMIT in his new name as HERU-UR and he took care of all the people with love and compassion.

He showed them how to live by MAAT (truth and justice).

HERU-UR showed them how to remember ASAR by always thinking of him when they eat and drink.

HERU UR told them that they should live in peace so that when they die they can go to live with ASAR in the kingdom of the afterlife forever and ever....

The two eyes of Heru became known as the essence of goodness, righteousness, courage and peace for generations to come.

Neru Heru! (Heru is the Victorious one!)
Neru Heru! (Heru is the Victorious one!)
Neru Heru! (Heru is the Victorious one!)
Neru Heru! (Heru is the Victorious one!)

Even today, every time the name of Heru is mentioned it brings a good feeling to the heart.

May the blessings of the eyes of Heru be with you always, especially in times of need. Whenever you need strength and courage and you don't know the right way to act, think of Heru and you will know the right way.

Dua Heru! (Adorations to Horus)
Dua Heru! (Adorations to Horus)
Dua Heru! (Adorations to Horus)
Dua Heru! (Adorations to Horus)

HERU-PA-KHRAT
(HERU the child –sitting on the lotus of Creation)

HERU asked ASET: "Mother, who am I and where do I come from?"

ASET answered: "HERU, my son, you, all people and all of the gods
and goddesses come from the Spirit of RA and you are a special
child because you will bring justice and truth to the world!"

HERU also became

Hery-shaf

Hery-shaf is the god of manliness- bravery - respect-he who is on his land.

Hery-shaf went around all the lands and with his great strength he helped people who were suffering, who were threatened, who were in fear.

He saved them from dangers, from monsters and from fear.

And Heru in his form of Hery-shaf was known by everyone as the god of goodness, peace and strength.

In the land of Greece he was called Hercules and throughout many generations the legend of Heru lived on, and on and now you know the great story of Asar Aset and Heru.

May the story of Asar Aset and Heru live on in You!

Who is Sebai Muata Abhaya Ashby D.D. Ph. D.?

Priest, Author, lecturer, poet, philosopher, musician, publisher, counselor and spiritual preceptor and founder of the Sema Institute-Temple of Aset, Muata Ashby was born in Brooklyn, New York City, and grew up in the Caribbean. His family is from Puerto Rico and Barbados. Displaying an interest in ancient civilizations and the Humanities, Sebai Maa began studies in the area of religion and philosophy and achieved doctorates in these areas while at the same time he began to collect his research into what would later become several books on the subject of the origins of Yoga Philosophy and practice in ancient Africa (Ancient Egypt) and also the origins of Christian Mysticism in Ancient Egypt.

Sebai Maa (Muata Abhaya Ashby) holds a Doctor of Philosophy Degree in Religion, and a Doctor of Divinity Degree in Holistic Health. He is also a Pastoral Counselor and Teacher of Yoga Philosophy and Discipline. Dr. Ashby received his Doctor of Divinity Degree from and is an adjunct faculty member of the American Institute of Holistic Theology. Dr. Ashby is a certified as a PREP Relationship Counselor. Dr. Ashby has been an independent researcher and practitioner of Egyptian Yoga, Indian Yoga, Chinese Yoga, Buddhism and mystical psychology as well as Christian Mysticism. Dr. Ashby has engaged in Post Graduate research in advanced Jnana, Bhakti and Kundalini Yogas at the Yoga Research Foundation. He has extensively studied mystical religious traditions from around the world and is an accomplished lecturer, musician, artist, poet, screenwriter, playwright and author of over 25 books on Kamitan yoga and spiritual philosophy. He is an Ordained Minister and Spiritual Counselor and also the founder the Sema Institute, a non-profit organization dedicated to spreading the wisdom of Yoga and the Ancient Egyptian mystical traditions. Further, he is the spiritual leader and head priest of the Per Aset or Temple of Aset, based in Miami, Florida. Thus, as a scholar, Dr. Muata Ashby is a teacher, lecturer and researcher. However, as a spiritual leader, his title is *Sebai,* which means Spiritual Preceptor.
Sebai Dr. Ashby began his research into the spiritual philosophy of Ancient Africa (Egypt) and India and noticed correlations in the culture and arts of the two countries. This was the catalyst for a successful book series on the subject called "Egyptian Yoga". Now he has created a series of musical compositions which explore this unique area of music from ancient Egypt and its connection to world music.

Made in the USA
Columbia, SC
23 September 2023

23245338R00030